In The Back of My Throat

)

Edited by

Norman Erikson Pasaribu
Tatevik Sargsyan

ANAMOT PRESS
London

Contents

Any kind of writing requires care,
humility and empathic inquiry.

Cathy Park Hong

)

In The Back
of My Throat

اله

Introduction

Norman Erikson Pasaribu and Tatevik Sargsyan

In The Back of My Throat encapsulates the visceral sensation of something stuck, choking on the queer softness of candy floss, the right words dissolving, the nuances of taste lost in translation—feelings all too familiar to those who navigate queerness. We're reminded of the mother of all curses: "Semoga duri ikan tersangkut di tenggorokanmu." I hope a fish bone gets stuck in your throat. Colonial history is the fish bone in our throat. Heteropatriarchy is the fish bone in our throat. Racial capitalism is the fish bone in our throat. While desperately trying to spit out these bones, we might wonder, discreetly, "What if I swallow these bones instead? But then, what will happen—to me?"

To resist is to live, to live is to celebrate. This book is our celebration of queer lives in Southeast Asia and its diaspora. In these pages, we explore the intersections of food and memory, language and translation, and history and queerness. In the act of remembering, we confront the complexities of our past, reshaping our understanding of self and community in the process. As we journey through these narratives, we are reminded that while we may not always recognise the path before us, we carry within us the echoes of our shared histories and the resilience to forge new ones. Decolonisation is the dream, always the dream, but can you ever sleep?

The spectrum of Southeast Asian queer experiences is as vast and intricate as the Indonesian archipelago itself. As the editors of this book, we acknowledge that we have only curated a ripple. We thank the British Council who helped fund this book, and to everyone who contributed to this anthology — the queers, the allies, and everyone journeying in between. We also acknowledge that many British institutions (such as the BBC, Oxford University Press and indeed the British Council) were set up to extend their colonial powers by imposing English language, literature and culture on local communities across countries they occupied.

Due to the oppressive efforts of the British having established linguistic imperialism, our shared language has inevitably become English. We use it as a bridge to allow us to be in dialogue and in community with Indonesian writers and Southeast Asian diasporas. We also foreground Indonesian translators who are able to reconnect with some of the 300 different native languages spoken in Indonesia.

This anthology is a testament to the experiences of queer communities, unbound by shame and fear, navigating the intersections of identity, culture, and colonial legacy. We don't need to reconcile our contrasting influences and identities. We are because and despite of what colonisers erased or enshrined. Through the prism of these stories, we offer a space to form and reform ourselves, somewhere to affirm our identities.

We can force the English language to bloom
in ways that it doesn't yet know it's capable of.

✣

Natalie Diaz

Cooking up [democracy dishes in my very own kitchen]
ko ko thett

What shall I cook for you people?
You can't afford to be a glutton
if you can't afford a grain of rice.
I will curry your revolution with coriander.
Simmer the mass movement until it gets
very, very soft — irreproachably tender.
I won't allow it to thicken, or it will be tasteless.
Turn social media into tomb and lemon salad.
I wouldn't garnish it with my three little fingers.
I will stir democracy dal with the longest
digit I possess. Let me pour out all my fish-sauce
feelings. Blood sploshes on the kitchen floor are of
no consequence. It's unavoidable.
I am the Executive Chef. Am I not a better cook
than your mother? I can ride a spatula for
a horse, yodelling like a hyena, under
a squeaky buffalo cart. The situation is plain
and simple, an elephant crumpling a paddy
in broad daylight — not just all the five abbots,
and the sangha mandapa, were overthrown;
even the reclining Buddha was knocked
down flat in the process. It's unavoidable.
You happened to be harvesting frogs in a
holey basket. The idiot lizar's ashen jacket will
collect nothing but ash. Don't take the burglar
creeping up on you from behind for your husband.
Please help yourself to Brussels sprouts and
Liberty Fries. Now let me serve up more bromides,
as soiled as my oily rags. I will investigate fraudulent
shopping lists, while you work up your appetite.
I have cooked with pots and pans, banged
out of shape, for your hunger-game protests.
After the state of emergency is over, there will be
a new election in the kitchen. I will then transfer
power to my shoe-in, Aloo Party for Our People.

Father's pistol belt

ko ko thett
Translated by kyi may kaung and ko ko thett

Smudged with blood
smeared with semen

not only does it hold up
father's pants

it also comes in handy
as a knout.

Holdover from
the Occupation,
with an expression of an immortal
what an affront
to Impermanence.

Like a turntable belt
it turns the world.

In its spare time
it coils like a snake,
ready to strike at whim.

Many heroes
war veterans
hanged by that belt.
Its length
the stretch
of an Empire —

in imperial measures

exactly —

thirty-eight inches

situational comedy: memorising the 99 Names of Allah through american sitcoms

Prahara Amelia
Translated by Madina Malahayati Chumaera

i am lulled in the backseat of america / every morning breakfasting fried rice and breakfarce rolls / every evening reciting qur'an in front of the tv / pancasila becoming a footnote in my duas before sleep / my shalat recitations with its many holes / i barter[ed] fairy tales in the closest language to God / at my age i then hadn't known / unlike night market stubs prayers couldn't be traded

i learnt [of love and loss | pity | war] the word "love" in the backseat of america / as mama's sedan drifted through nevada / i was busy looking for God / the same way i chased the moon from the car window / my eyes stitching the electric poles and wires that wound the sky / impatiently waiting for God to stop by reno, nevada / i wanted to whisper to heads bowing in las vegas chapels / and to the lips drinking in the green of mountain dew in front of 7-11 / i want a God who loves me even when He hates me.

i'm still sitting in the backseat of america / waiting for the right time / to peel my skin off, one by one / to parsing [this] vocabulary / until the friends theme song is stamped no longer in the back of my throat / as i am scared the librarian who lent their fairy tale [story book] to me / will collect this debt / the language they lent when i landed in soekarno-hatta / when what i wanted to say was: america and i / both forgot / how to offer a prayer / that does not start with "I."

Queering the Old Age: Sex Worker

Nurdiyansah and Mak Lin in conversation
Translated by Norman Erikson Pasaribu

Her name is Lina Pontia, but we call her Mak Lin. I got to know Mak Lin through Mama Atha, a mother and trans artist who is also a member of the Seroja Studio. When I saw Mak Lin for the first time, it was a hot day and she met us without any makeup, wearing a simple T-shirt and shorts. I was struck by her gentle mannerism. She lived in the well-known Kampung Duri, West Jakarta, along with other trans women, of all ages, who came from numerous professions. Mak Lin was sixty-two when this interview was held in 2022.

My first meeting with Mak Lin was remarkable. Even though we only spent the afternoon chatting around a grocery stall in a residential alley not far from the Duri Station, the friendly atmosphere in the urban Kampung was so pleasing. People greeted us as we passed them by. We received no stares or slurs during our little trip through the snake-like alleyways that were squeezed between semi-permanent, two-floor buildings. All the houses in the Kampung were no bigger than a 4x4 room. Some were even smaller. With wooden walls and tin roofs, these houses can host a little family inside. Here, in this alley, Mak Lin lives alone, or technically not alone—if we consider the trans community who has put its roots there and is one of the essential parts of Kampung Duri. Some members of the community have been friends with Mak Lin for decades and some have a special familial bond with her, and she calls them "my kids".

On our second meeting, I asked Mak Lin if she would be interested in the idea of putting her life and her lived experience as a sex worker into writing. As if this was just a daily request, she immediately said yes. I was a bit surprised at first, but then I thought: the life of a sex worker is indeed a daily matter. We needed to admit that sex work wasn't limited to the night service between a sex worker and their client, but other sexually related services that were significant in our life. For example, since I was little, I knew that my father liked to buy and collect porn magazines. In elementary school, I watched a blue film that my friend's parents owned. Even now, I have an appreciation for what people would call adult films, or the sexy dancers in the clubs, or erotic visual artworks.

It's true though, things that have been a part of our lives and should have been seen as normal, sometimes can't escape from the confinement of other people's morality. Stigma and discrimination are still attached to sex workers. Even though Indonesia doesn't have the regulations that explicitly ban sex work (which is why one can insist that a sex worker can't be convicted), sex workers are often criminalised and vulnerable to violence.

A lot of the debate regarding this issue shouldn't be severed from the fact that a sex worker's right is also a human right, and is also the legal right of all citizens.

On our second meeting, Mak Lin and I chatted in Mama Atha's house. She told me that she spent her formative years in Pontianak, West Kalimantan, and she is of Dayak and Melayu descent. When she was little, she wanted to be a teacher. "I want to educate kids to be good people," she explained. It led her to pursue a Teacher's School–equal to high school. She started teaching when she was still studying. What follows is an abridged transcript of our conversation, where I learnt about Mak Lin's lifetime pursuit of teaching and educating others in her unique way. Our discussion is interspersed with some additional explanatory information, in italics, where I have summarised and contextualised other details that Mak Lin shared with me.

NURDIYANSAH
Mak Lin, how did you discover yourself? And when did you start expressing yourself as a woman?

MAK LIN
I have eight siblings, and all of them are women, I was the only boy. Since I was in elementary school, I liked to be around girls. All of my siblings disapproved of this, but I insisted. In middle school, I fell in love with a boy. After getting in touch with some of my trans neighbours, I decided to start dating men. Well, my mother's friends were all queer, I just joined them on their dress-up-and-date routine.

NURDIYANSAH
Dress-up-and-date?

MAK LIN
I would dress up and go out at night to look for clients, flirting with men. I was 16 back then and had left school, I took my chances and would even explore bigger roads.

NURDIYANSAH
When you were at school, did you experience discrimination or bullying?

MAK LIN
Never. In Pontianak, it's so common to be trans. All the cis mothers there mingled with us transwomen. No such thing as bullying.

NURDIYANSAH
What did your parents think when you started dressing-up?

MAK LIN
My parents were angry because I stopped going to school. So I explained to them that even if I finished my studies, being a sex worker would still be the life that I want. My parents said, "OK, you can do whatever you want, as long as it is good for you."

NURDIYANSAH
So when did you move to Jakarta?

MAK LIN
In 1982. For quite some time, I had been dressing-up in Singkawang, on the Malaysian border, and then to Palembang, and then Ketapang... I followed my friends to work on the ships. Many transwomen worked on the ships as cooks. When the ships threw their anchors somewhere, I would dress-up-and-date in the harbours.

The Entikong Border separates Malaysian Sarawak to Indonesian Sanggau, West Kalimantan. Mak Lin was born and grew up in this province. Aside from doing sex work in Malaysia, in 1981 she also worked on a ship, in the kitchen. She said that at that time there were no special requirements, or even required documents, to be a cook on a ship. "You just need to do it" she said. It was a trans friend who invited her to take up this job; this friend was also her senior on the ship. Mak Lin spent two years of her life on this ship. Cooking for the deckhands, her salary was small, but she got the chance to visit bigger ports and harbours, like the Sunda Kelapa Harbour, the Gresik Port, and the Tanjung Perak Port—this latter port was where she would hang around and wait for clients.

NURDIYANSAH
What was it like for transwomen who offer sex work around the harbour?

MAK LIN
In the harbour, I would never have to worry about getting raided by the police. We hung around there just for the workers of the harbour because outsiders weren't allowed to enter. The port officials were kind to us because they knew we were cooks on the ships. Even outside sex workers couldn't get in. Too many mosquitos, though. While we were there, we would chat with our friend or partner for the night, and we wouldn't have to fear any police raids. We could do it behind the porter's office, or anywhere in the port—as long as it was vacant or had a lot of shrubs. We couldn't bring our clients to the ships. We could also befriend other trans cooks. At that time, you could find many trans cooks because there weren't a lot of requirements to be able to work on ships, as long as you could cook, were diligent and didn't get seasick. Usually, there were twenty transwomen cooks on a ship. Meanwhile, the deckhands came from anywhere: Palembang, Maluku, etc. So, after we finished cooking dinner, we would dress up, disembark in the evening, and hang around at the harbour.

NURDIYANSAH
What's an unforgettable experience from when you worked on the ship, as a cook and as a sex worker?

MAK LIN
Whenever we were going to throw the anchor all I could think about was disembarking to wait for clients. Sometimes our loyal clients worked on the same ships, so we knew each other well and made an appointment to meet somewhere at the port. To be paid or not to be paid—it all depended on our agreement. One of the sweet memories was dating a deckhand. When they got their monthly salary, sometimes they gave us money or took us out and bought us things. We cooked for them and also treated them with care.

NURDIYANSAH
What were your expectations, as a transwoman, when you decided to be a sex worker?

MAK LIN
When I am doing my work [as a sex worker], I feel I am a woman... that I can get to know a guy, can talk with him, flirt with him. I feel womanly. That's why I did it.

NURDIYANSAH
Do you have any special reason to be a sex worker?

MAK LIN
I worked because I liked it. And then, I wanted to be financially independent from my parents. I left school, and I could still live without their help. My parents said, "You can do whatever you want, as long as you can pay for your own roof, do everything yourself." So, yeah, I did it because it was satisfactory and paid my bills.

NURDIYANSAH
What kind of satisfaction?

MAK LIN
Physical needs. And then, inner needs. I was pleased because I got to talk with men that liked me. Well, if he didn't like you, he probably needed money [from you]. But when you liked each other, you could talk all day.

NURDIYANSAH
You started doing this when you were 16 years old. And now you are 62 years old. Are you still a sex worker?

MAK LIN
Yes. Now, I work twice a week.

NURDIYANSAH
And at your age now, are your reasons for doing this work the same as before?

MAK LIN
Yes. The older we get, the more fervent our physical needs.

NURDIYANSAH
Do you get any age related discrimination, for example, has anyone ever said that you are too old to be a sex worker?

MAK LIN
From fellow transwomen, no. The Jembatan Besi, where we usually gathered—I was among the first sex workers doing business there. So, fellow sex workers can't alienate me. Some of them are just like my own kids.

They respected me because I was one of the pioneers there. Meanwhile, non-trans people would tell me, "Come on, Mak, retire! Stop staying up so late at night. You are old!" These were usually the younger men, who were also still out late at night. So my response was: who cares! They clapped, so I clapped back.

In Jakarta, Mak Lin waited for her first clients in the Fatahillah area in Kota Tua—to be exact, beside the Kali Besar (Great River) that people used to call "Kaliber". The area once had a lively nightlife—bars and other kinds of entertainment. However, after Kota Tua changed its image into an area of cultural conservation and a tourist destination, Mak Lin and three of her colleagues moved to Jembatan Besi. They started going there dressed-up. Their clients there were usually working-class and came from all kinds of professions.

NURDIYANSAH
Do you have a partner now?

MAK LIN
I used to have one. But after the pandemic, I chose not to. It's tiring!

NURDIYANSAH
Do you have any kids or relatives?

MAK LIN
I never had a wife. But I have a nephew who lives in my hometown, who will take care of me one day.

NURDIYANSAH
In your opinion, is there any difference between a trans and cis sex worker?

MAK LIN
Trans sex workers have their own ways to satisfy their clients. We can do all kinds of games very well: the oral game, the anal game, the hand game… But, still, there are various kinds of transwomen too.

The rate for sex workers in Jembatan Besi was around IDR 50.000-100.000 (2.50-5 GBP) for a short session. According to Mak Lin, price differences occurred not always because of the physical look of the sex workers, or their age, but also their hospitality towards the clients. Mak Lin, however, only charged her clients IDR 50.000 at most—due to her older age. Sometimes, she wouldn't mind doing her service for a lower amount of money if the men were much younger than her and if she also liked those men. "For younger men, I'd even do it for IDR 20.000. For older men, sometimes I said no even if it's for IDR 100.000. Because I don't like older men," she said.

Based on her experience, she said that younger men often prefer older sex workers because older sex workers weren't fussy and would do their service slowly.

NURDIYANSAH
What are your worries as you grow older? Considering that Indonesians often see elderly people as retirees who would spend everyday with their children and grandchildren—in reality, not all elderly can afford to do that...

MAK LIN
I have things to worry about, yeah. Everyone does. I accepted everything and went wherever the water carried me. If I die in this city, I am okay to be buried here. If I still get to go back to my hometown, then I will go. I'd accept everything. We live or die tomorrow, no one knows.

NURDIYANSAH
What do you worry about?

MAK LIN
I am afraid to see God because I haven't done enough things in my life. I haven't done enough good deeds. I'm not afraid of anything else.

NURDIYANSAH
What do you see as good deeds?

MAK LIN
Like the five-times prayer, or sharing what I have with the have-not... I haven't done this a lot. I didn't get a lot of time to recite the Quran or do fasting because I always had to work during the night. So, I have so many things to improve. If I am given a long life and health, I will repent. Oh, this doesn't mean I will stop being trans though. I will always be a woman. What I meant was I might stop working so late at night, and focus more on my faith, and not spend all of my time with men.

Mak Lin said that when she reaches sixty-five years old—which means three years from the time of our chat—she wants to come back to her hometown in Pontianak. She has a lot of relatives there. She said she was willing to help them with anything, including their businesses.

NURDIYANSAH
What is the biggest challenge of being elderly?

MAK LIN
Our declining physical capabilities and then how we're so invisible whenever we dress up or wait for clients. Nobody pays us any attention. Even if we sang door to door, people wouldn't bother to think of giving us some money.

NURDIYANSAH
What are your aspirations or demands, looking at the working conditions of sex workers here; and how they face stigma, violence, and discrimination?

MAK LIN
Please don't alienate trans sex workers. We are just human beings who also need to eat, need to be happy—just like everyone else. Don't be violent to us because we also have families and relatives. What if your children decided to transition? To my fellow trans sex workers, work well and respectfully. Try to not fight with your clients. Manage your money because you might face hardship when you are older. To non-sex workers, respect our work. Treat us as friends.

*

A Toilet Guide for Younger Indonesian Transmen

C. Abrisam

Translated by Norman Erikson Pasaribu

"Bang, do you use the men's bathroom? I've doubts about it. Is it true that they shot the whole of *The Exorcist* there?"

I am often bombarded with these questions by younger transmen, who have just recently accepted and started expressing their identities. In our trans circle, I consider myself among the lucky ones, because I can freely use the bathrooms that fit my gender identity, which are the men's bathrooms. Even so, I am still haunted by the ghosts of what-might-happen, fearing them quite intensely—I mean, with cismen who knows what kind of violence is around the corner. Sometimes, I agonise over the idea of going inside the bathroom. I know many transmen might feel the same.

Yeah, I worry that cis people would become suspicious of my being, or feel that my physical characteristics aren't quite cis-passing. I also worry that they would find out that I don't have a penis because I was born as a female. On the other hand, the men's bathrooms—at least in Jakarta, where I live—are utterly disgusting. I take pity on how dirty they are.

However, I survived them and now I want to share the dos and don'ts of men's bathrooms in Jakarta. I feel the need to be specific so you, too, can steer clear of all the demons inside them.

My first point, and the most important one: please understand that most cismen in Indonesia are still subscribed to toxic masculinity, which provides the bread and butter of our bathroom affair. You, a transman, should exploit it. Yes—exploit cismen's toxic masculinity, without having to echo it. Remember! You can use it! All you need is a little bit of a role play, and all of your bathroom affairs will never get clogged up like Jakarta's evening traffic.

The rule of thumb is to bring your support system inside if you still feel too anxious. It is recommended that you are aware of your physical distance and how you interact with your chosen friend. Being so intensely close with him inside the bathroom might be seen as "excessively gay" for Jakartan cismen—which might lead to a sneer or worse, violence.

Even though you have made your decision, you might still worry about being watched, examined or rejected by these cismen. It might be still fresh in your memory of how some time ago, in the women's bathroom, you were also being watched by ciswomen, scolded, and then eventually expelled. You might still feel traumatised by being mistaken by ciswomen as a perverted cisman when you decided to express yourself masculinely that day. You still remember how some of these ciswomen stood in front of the mirror near the entrance of the bathroom, staring at and judging anyone who entered.

But, have no worries! This won't happen in the male toilets. As a species who upholds masculinity with such commitment, Indonesian cismen won't spend too much time gathering and doing small talk in front of a toilet mirror. For them, this activity would reduce their manliness because they often hear this happening in the women's toilets. If there are men doing this, they would be considered gay. Indonesian cismen need to stay manly 86% of the time, and the remaining 14% is their allocated time for sleep. All the male gazes on the toilet have to be glances. If you feel the need to ponder, look at the floor or the empty wall. Count the parading ants.

Cismen will also get easily offended if they feel they're being looked at, or if they accidentally share a glance with another person in the toilet. To accommodate their fragility, be cool for them. Think of yourself as an object, like a piece of wood in the park—so invisible, bypassed.

One of the things you need to remember when you use the men's bathroom is that cismen embrace their filthiness. Sometimes you would find pubic hair inside the toilet or splashes of yellowish water, fresh or dried. Or even footprints on the toilet seat. Not to mention, the missing toilet paper—remember to bring your own. I guess, as long as you haven't started your hormone therapy, you could just pick any toilet where you'll feel the most comfortable.

Some transmen I know told me that they switched to a feminine way of talking whenever they get nudged at the women's bathroom. Others try to only use unisex or accessible toilets. Some even choose to resist the urge to use public toilets and hold on a little bit longer until they arrive home, which would definitely lead to more problems.

Ugh. So much ugh. In an equal world, we really don't have to worry about all these issues.

If you are menstruating, the challenge manifests when it's time to change your pad. The noise from taking off the pad from your underwear—the "Skrttttt!!!"—can attract unnecessary attention. Be free by adding even louder noises, use the flush, turn on the faucet beside the toilet seat, or buy a second phone, and call yourself. Bring a plastic bag for your disposals. There are rumours that the bins in men's toilets differ from the ones you'd find in the women's toilets. But who has the time to validate this? What if some of you still don't have the courage to use the men's toilets? How do you adapt to a city that doesn't accommodate you?

Of The Borders I (Cannot) Cross: The Queer (Im)possibilities
Pychita Julinanda

I don't feel good... in these.

I looked in the mirror and I did not quite recognise myself. I was dressed in a plain black shirt, plain black tailored trousers, and some silver jewellery. These were some of the few items of masculine clothing I had, and that day I felt masculine. That day's gender was masculine. I wanted to look masculine. I wanted people to recognise the masculine streak that I put quite an effort into expressing. I wanted people to call me a boy, because I felt like a boy that day.

So why did I feel even more dysphoric in these clothes?

I had been out as gender fluid for almost a year and had rarely made an attempt to pass as masculine. I had convinced myself that I had achieved gender euphoria, that I did not feel an ounce of body dysphoria. I had always liked the way my body wrapped my being, the way it allowed me to play around with clothes and styles, textures and colours, and my body hadn't changed much since I embraced myself in a new light.

It had been a pleasant transition. The first time, a thought passed through my mind—this isn't it all—I was conscious of a vague idea buzzing in the back of my mind. This isn't all of me. Oh sure, like half of my generation, this realisation was accompanied by ripples in my TikTok algorithm, as my feed was flooded with gender fluid creators—many of them a few years younger than me. This was the true Gen Z, as they say, born in the new millennium of the 2000s, speaking fluently in edits, funky lighting, and transitions (pun not intended). Unlike me, the faux-millennial, pseudo-Gen Z, born just in the peripheral border of the millennium with enough understanding of Gen Z's language but never the full ability to speak it. On my TikTok, they were speaking a language I didn't expect to resonate with: the fluidity of gender.

I began exploring the shape-shifting of figures; the constant reinvention of the self, and most thrillingly the playfulness within the lines of gender borders— the total joyous giddiness of claiming gender as a playground rather than a battlefield. I remembered tweeting, "guys, I think I might be...gender fluid?" and a dear friend reached out to talk it through with me. I called another friend and told them how liberating it was to recognise myself under the trans flag—how it had been painful to be a woman full of rage and battle against the men, and how joyous it was then to think of gender as just some silly thing you could hop around in, play with, and make a performance of. I was welcomed by fellow non-binary folks and their gender journey helped me with mine. It was euphoric.

I looked in the mirror, and my head automatically started picking out the ugly things I saw. My breasts were still visible, failing to be hidden under the cheap sports bra I bought online. My shoulders were not broad and defined, but narrow and hunched under a shirt that could actually be menacingly handsome on a person with defined shoulders. I saw my soft flesh which was the result of depression-induced disordered eating, and my hips which were not pointed enough to effect a masculine shape. My silver jewellery didn't contribute to a sense of androgyny, it only framed my cleavage with the way it hung in the middle of my breasts.

It was impossible to pass.

It was impossible to convince people that I wasn't really a woman—let alone a boy. My gender fluidity had reached its glass ceiling that it could not surpass, a border I could not cross. Not with this body.

The first time—another first time—I heard my friend say in all the glorious sass of a transmasc, "Well yeah, I might be a cowok, but I am a cowok ngondek," another electric shock jolted through my soul. Yes, that's it, the idea buzzed in me, now clearer than ever before. I am a cowok ngondek!

My expression of gender fluidity had been a bit vague. I had used any pronouns, avoided any clear definition of my identity, thinking it was always in flux depending on my mood each day.

I remembered my cishet male co-worker asking, "how do I know if you're (being) a boy or a girl today?" and I couldn't find an easy answer, "just look at the clothes I'm wearing for the day," but it never had been that simple. Sometimes I found myself waking up to an anxiety of not being able to define the sense of self I wanted to settle in that day. I had thought of these days as one of my "neutral days", but the crippling dread of not matching what I felt in the interior and what I presented on the exterior of my flesh left a lingering discomfort.

It was a dizzying mismatch, reminding me of my mother's voice when she used to police what I wore. Everyday, I found being regarded in feminine honorifics more and more repulsive. That was not me. I was not an mbak.

I was so much more than simply an mbak. I was more than the high-pitched voice I spoke with, the breasts visible on my body. Sure, the fact that I used all pronouns meant folks were not wrong to call me mbak, but had they even considered I wanted to use other pronouns, too? Had they even glimpsed the masculine streak in me, that indicated I might want to be called mas? Had they even tried? But it then dawned on me. Maybe the streak of masculinity I presented meant that I was only a cewek tomboy—almost a boy, but not quite fully a boy.

As my friend's voice replayed over and over in my head—I am a cowok ngondek—the electric joy of this phrase brought me to a euphoric state once more, just like the first time I heard these words. I was not a girl (cewek), definitely not a cewek tomboy. I was, I had discovered, a cowok ngondek. I smiled to myself as I announced it to the whole world (meaning, a group of my loved ones), I am a cowok ngondek and they had smiled, too, ah, yes, of course you are. You laugh like one. I laughed, just to savour the way I did.

No matter how hard I tried to pass, dressed in the most dull, colourless, plain masculine clothing, people would still call me mbak.

The more I tried to silently beg people not to address me as a girl, the more hurtful it felt when they still did so. Even when I wore a cheap sports bra or a too-tight bra that nearly broke my ribs and triggered my acid reflux, even when I spent my last cash of the month to cut my hair, even when I paid extra to cut my hair in a high-end, predominantly male barbers, they still saw me as the breasts that showed, and heard me in my high-pitched voice. It felt like they intentionally refused to hear my silent plea to recognise the masculinity I was trying to present. The pain in my nearly broken ribs stung tenfold each time I was addressed in feminine honorifics, my lungs screaming—take it off! Take it off! I had a ringing question in my head—who are you doing this for? It all felt so painful, and so in vain.

As I was faced with such queer impossibility, I felt a kick in my chest—this was dysphoria, the very thing I had convinced myself did not shape my trans experience. But what should I do? Today I just wanted someone, just one person, to call me ganteng. One nod of recognition and the burn marks in my chest would be worth the pain. So I sighed in front of the mirror, and went on my way.

To inhabit the borderlands of gender is to be filled with (im)possibilities: to flow, to seep, and to break free. Existing in the very borders of gender binary—even toying with it and hopping along the lines—was at times filled with euphoria. The silly giddiness of breaking yet another expectation; the playful queer possibilities of being all the things I want, just because I can. This did not feel at all possible when I still identified as a cis woman caught up in the 'battle of the sexes'.

Yet now, identifying as gender fluid, I am not the liberatory rebel punching authorities left and right with my own fists, a hero we often see in fiction. I fear for my safety and my community's, and in these times when it is tough to be trans, none of us are free to swing our punches in any way—we are at the receiving end of those punches. I can't help but cower in the face of such impossible position. I am shrouded with cowardly shame when I state the reasons why I am yet to take T, as I am hiding behind my privileges of passing as a cis woman.

Transfems as well as visibly feminine (effeminate) men are one of the most vulnerable groups, and are easy targets of violence in my society. I would be obliterated to pieces in public if I were to dress up, put on makeup, and gesture and speak in such a ngondek manner when I pass as a man. I would put myself financially at risk even more than I do now,—its very hard to find a stable job and a house to rent with my ID card showing a different gender identity to my gender presentation. Even as someone who passes as a cis woman, I can barely pay my rent and bills each month.

If I were to medically transition, I would jeopardise my fragile relationship with my mother, again, after years of estrangement and some little months of superficial reconciliation—she is my only safety net and I am the only precious little one she has. Medical transition would mean putting myself at a worse risk of violence and precarity, and I can't help but shiver in fear. I feel terribly shameful of my fear, unable to surpass this impasse, queer impossibilities spread out into multiple branches from each one queer possibility I discovered. As a trans-masculine, T is a border I can't cross, and I weep in grief.

Identifying as a woman meant I was born of pain, it being my sole inheritance that I had to carry throughout my life. For my sake, for my mother's sake, our shared curse. It was fate. So I screamed and I fought and I spat blood at men to make them see what they have done. As filmmaker and writer Jonah Wu put it, I was a woman warrior with femininity as my armour, a mantle of defence and a wielded knife of offense. I connected with other (cis) women this way, too. We trauma-bonded over our shared curse, at the same time not knowing how to build real intimacy without it. Femininity to me has always been full of anger and resentment of the arduous fate I had to endure.

To have all the queer possibilities laid in front of me is to break free of that fate, I can allow myself to cross out my inheritance of womanhood, and I am not defined by it anymore. I am allowed to breathe and caress myself softly, basking in gentle masculinity. I don't have to fight anymore. My armour is laid down and my knife is now chopping food I prepared with so much love to feed my dear ones. Masculinity is my capacity to love, build intimacy, hug and kiss and share my affection with people around me.

These are some of the things I would like to be known for. Masculinity is the capacity to rage at the right space, to know how to protect my precious ones without engaging in thoughtless rampage and directionless self-defence. Masculinity offers a bright childlike curiosity for what the world has to offer, and the joyous exploration of it all is available free of chaining burdens. Femininity is now something I love to perform, a stage where my masculinity explores its stylistic features. I am the feminine masculine, the fluid being, the shape-shifter, the stateless unterritorial entity in rebellion against the nature of things.

Gardenly Father: KM 15

Kristal Firdaus
Translated by Ziggy Zezsyazeoviennazabrizkie

I am the little man of the house
I have no interest in doing manly chores
or sweating a manly sweat

gas cylinders in the kitchen scare me
football escapes me—real or fantasy

all I have on gardening I got
from western movies: glamorous, in a backyard or front,
with greens to pick fresh for our daily dishes.
While, for Father, gardening is [1] a plod
through a winding road, whose turns I could never recall.
As the plantation stretched far, I fell asleep
and sometimes even songs couldn't keep away the sheep

[2] to carry a scythe, bottled water, and a pesticide
everywhere. The world advances and Father's
hands are no longer occupied—still his back
cracks with the weight of our garden

Slashing the weeds, slashing the soil,
Father is but a child in the garden of God
and beneath the Trees, we all are permanent guests

it's only Sundays for me
it's Father's everydays
to sow the field and forget the rest
Father gardens through his waking hours

Father is wilting
he is coming to the Trees
to the garden of God
trudging towards deliverance
sweating a manly sweat, in his manly vigour

O Trees, receive my Father, now and ever
though the earth crumbles as Father
plants more and more palm trees

O Trees, receive my Father, now and ever
I do not play football
but I do pray with my all

What does it mean to be nourished?
Pear Nuallak

if you swallowed the moon,   feasting on   secret nacreous innards,

i think it would feel like stealing   something   closed inside its house,

a cool slice of melon   that's   soft and hard, rinded ownership

or maybe   slipping   splitting, dreaming impossibly

a hard-boiled egg, peeled   away   descending beyond knowledge

Every gathering, personal and political, must have food on the table. It is an essential component of conspiring, mourning and celebrating with comrades. What can be done on an empty belly?

I've been to trans dinners, ACAB Cafés, queer picnics, autonomous street parties, QTIPOC cabaret nights. Sometimes shyness prevents me from approaching the food, but it's still comforting to know it's there. When I enter a certain type of community space, I know there will be rows of tea mugs and a bottle of squash. Also in attendance are half-eaten bags of rice cakes, each one thinly curled over itself; if there's a bigger event, the rice cakes will be embarrassed by their proximity to good bread, generously heaped platters of rice, salads, stuffed vegetables, and all manner of things lavished with attention and seasoning. It's humble yet abundant. Sometimes I am the one who sets out the rice cakes, washes up the tea mugs, and wipes up the crumbs. If I go to a place that brands itself as being for community but considers squash beneath itself, I cannot feel truly welcome there.

My father cooked for our family. He may have cooked for yours, too. For most of his years in London, he's worked in a kitchen, like many Thai migrants. Because he arrived in Thatcher's England on a favourable visa and views the world as the rise and fall of individual actors finding (or losing) their rightful places in society, he associates her regime with opportunity and freedom. The anti-racism and union organising of the 80's did not interest either of my parents: they saw themselves as highly trained artists who arrived in Wimbledon to paint the murals at Buddhapadipa temple. Once this devotional act was complete, British race and class structures pushed them into service work. Thus, they became part of Thailand's outward labour supply that feeds and looks after Britain while enduring its colonial violences—which they sympathise with. They delight in "pure Englishness" and resent others who don't. From childhood they instilled in me the belief that my body was simply an extension of theirs, an outgrowth to be worried over and ordered into a sufficiently polite Thai-ness ("riiap-roi") yielded to authority (the family, the nation, the king).

My parents simultaneously insisted on my British-ness, which they saw as uncorrupted, with free and easy life choices: the West was a place where dreams could be realised without the social order they also paradoxically craved. Such contradictions were simply our family philosophy; it took many years to be able to contextualise this as Buddhist Nationalism tangled up with a highly idiosyncratic understanding of Western liberalism.

While my parents are open and friendly to everybody, their beliefs about how society should be organised do not align with this. My parents particularly enjoyed making white English friends as it was proof they could assimilate; the fact that nearly all of said friends have stopped speaking to them on account of being dead or having embraced racism more closely in recent years is a cause for mourning.

One such friend was a Scottish organist who was one of the first people to hold me when I was just born. I remember his white eyebrows and how upsettingly long his coffin was at his funeral. My parents organised a memorial at Buddhapadipa temple. My father roasted and then carved a chicken, pulling it apart, his fingers glossy with its juices when he greeted someone's arrival in the kitchen. Later, his hands were dusted pale as he deposited his late friend's ashes into the temple rose garden—with respectful delicacy at first, then with the matter-of-fact vigour of an experienced gardener applying nourishment to the soil.

To the delight of my mother, my hands are a smaller version of her husband. Everything my mother likes about me is also a feature of my father, his brow, his hands, his voice, his various skills. My flaws are all hers, her sturdy figure, shortness of leg and temper. She loves telling friends that I have the skillset of a good wife: cooking and textiles, an interest in making things for the home. As far as she's concerned, I am very successful at my assigned gender: wife. My mother has no idea that I mainly use these skills alongside other queer people in an attempt to make a liveable future outside of the structure of the capitalist heteronormative family.

At our queer community hub we always have free food. The attempts to expel trans people from public life, the increasing privatisation of public space, housing precarity, queerphobic family and social isolation of migrants means there is an urgent need for gathering places.

Our hub is located in the open-plan kitchen of a local community centre. People can come to us the hours just before night shelters open so they can sit with us in a warm place, charge their phones, and share food. This is not charity: we are redistributing things so members of our community can get what they need.

The kitchen is at the centre of these needs. Like most community kitchens, it is a comfortingly practical place (lino floor, big fridges, colour-coded chopping board signs high above). It always smells faintly of cleaning spray and biscuits with a hint of coffee granules. A hot water urn rumbles in the corner. We lay our spread on the island, our hot drink selection in serried ranks, fresh fruit and snacks alongside leaflets of local queer-friendly services laid on a pride flag.

On the other side of the kitchen we push some tables together so everyone can gather round. People sit down with a hot mug of something, herb tea or instant pasta, and munch on digestives, plantain crisps, vegan sweets in rainbow colours. At Christmas, the Outside Project, a grassroots queer homeless community centre and shelter, fully activates this kitchen for a festive community lunch, its two ovens roasting at capacity.

My friends know I will take up residence in their kitchen if they invite me round. From my vantage point at the stove, I hear all the gossip; I see someone bringing a batch of homemade pickles, and another, and yet another. (Queer home ferments are big this year). I like knowing that nobody will go hungry. Being in the kitchen at house parties makes me think of those rare family trips to Thailand. My father would take it upon himself to cook for his friends, all of them graduates of the same art school; unlike my father they spent the past decade building careers as successful artists in Thailand rather than trying to survive as migrants in England.

Occasionally they would upset my father with an ignorant remark about his job. Regardless, my father cooked a steak and told me to take it to his friends, and I resented that I was a girl-seeming creature before middle-aged men, that nobody wanted to thank my father for his effort. I, who had been fed by him every day of my life, didn't understand this ingratitude. But my father was delighted to be surrounded by friends and food. Now that I have grown into friends and comrades of my own, I understand my father a little more.

Where Rot Lives

Anna Sulan Masing

The tropics is a place where rot resides and exists side by side - neigh is intertwined with - flourish, growth and abundance.

Everything disintegrates in the heat. The weight of the jungle feels ready to take over, even in the heart of the city. Encompassing. Ants devour the minute residue of toothpaste on my toothbrush, creating trails up the bathroom wall.

Pork is cooked in my family's kitchen, cooked and cooked till dry. So it will withstand rot for some time, will last longer. Belachan – fermented shrimp paste - sits at the side of many dishes, or, folded through. The heart of banana flowers, soft boiled, a little like an artichoke heart, lightly covered in the salty, sharp, spiced and delicious rotting aquatic life.

The forest floor is coated in the dead leaves of trees. The big architectural shapes of tropical plants, deep, deep green, become discarded brown on the ground. Soggy in shape as they disintegrate into the soil. The damp soil, soaked with the heavy rain drops of the night before. Mushrooms of detailed, intricate design sprout from the broth of earth. Nestled in under a shadow of the canopy. A rotten log, a branch from a tree, crosses the path - to be clambered over - and another family of mushrooms grow, sated by the rot.

In the depth of the rotting layers of forest debris, a nest of eggs. The parent stands astride this dug-in den. The lizard waits for us to pass; protecting. The warmth of the decaying forest floor creates the perfect incubator.
The heat of rot. Microbial breakdown of jungle waste. The act of rot, composing new life.

I visit my father on Gawai, the harvest festival for us Dayak, the indigenous of this land. He's covered in concrete, soon to be marble. No rot here. Just disintegration. The fight against nature as we memorialise him in building things that cannot, or are slow to, rot; Borneo Iron Wood will line the place, a space for us to come to speak to him. Ritualising space.

We pour tuak - fermented (rotting) rice, made into a drink - out for him, take a sip ourselves. Cry, salty tears at the cruelty of absence and of the abundance of life we feel.

I tell him about the things I will be doing - the vigour in which I am going forth.

Salt, curing. Saline solutions that suspend rot.

Grief is ferment. It sits, it bubbles, it has a known process but doesn't always follow the rules. It is, ingredients in a jar: salt, maybe some sugar. Spice. Preserving. Disintegration of fibres. A transformation.

Sipping on tiga masam: calamansi limes, lemon and sour plum - a fruit dried and preserved with sugar and salt, that comes to life in this drink. Eeking out its flavour with the water. The acidity of the citrus cuts through the heat, a touch of salt in the drink is reviving. Refreshed from preservation. The citrus cures me. Sipping and sipping on the drink after visiting the gravesite.

Sun and sweat. The awareness of a body in space, heavy. Wading through. Mulch of the humid air.

Where rot lives, life thrives.

***

When travelling, flying over the globe, the world below looks like a flourishing petri dish – dots on a film. I have travelled so many miles, from one island country to another. Even my place of original birth is an island – the enormity of Australia belies its island-ness, but it is a floating landmass. I say 'original', as it is technically my place of birth but it has no reflection on the person I am today; it did not birth me. I have been birthed many times, in many places, made whole in different spaces. Been made undone, heart-broken, realities rocked, futures crushed, only to find new ways to anchor myself. To discard a skin of existence and find new home, new life.

Borneo, New Zealand, the British isle. Surrounded by seas. Islands in brine, soaking in the remnants of what passes through. Some things stay. Coming back to this island, the Greatness of Britain feels remote as the fight for leadership of a government that has done nothing but let rot set in.

Rot that erodes rights; the years of the pandemic when people – when black and brown bodies - are allowed to not matter. When not just individuals, but whole communities, are left aside to fend of the rot of a system that forgets. That death chases those that do not have.

Hunger also chases. The need for food banks are on a steady increase. The liberal cling to the concept of class, strapping on an identity, a sensibility that is linked exclusively to a history that they are no longer a part of. There is a sense that working class is a static identity to be passed down generations, despite a movement in circumstance. Therefore, when inequality is shown, when rot that does not provide life is uncovered, there is an ease of turning ones head if it is not effecting ones' life.

In pandemic times the working class, the class that laboured, where migrants, left to languish. There was a fight to be recognised as bodies with agency. In an office a cleaner, in the parliamentary buildings, died because rights were not recognised.

It drips, this sort of rot, from the top. The froth of wine – fermented grapes – from parties. Illegal parties, a decaying system performed by grotesque figures bloated on self-belief. Laughter echoes, the bouffon takes the stage and we are forced to clap. The drip turns into cascades and now we don't know how to stop it. The centre left has drunk from the bacchanalia and now we have politicians dictating How To Be A Woman. Gender seems unrelated to a conservative capitalism, class and race, but it is all part of this idea to strip bodies of agency, of reclamation, and allowing difference to be celebrated and nurtured. Eradicating community.

From this rot there is no refuge. The system rots and we desperately try to dig in the dirt to find life, to restore ourselves. This rot seems to kill life.

***

The summer has brought weeks of rain. My London garden smells damp, the mulch of fallen leaves mingling with the store bought compost.

The garden has struggled, but this year we took it on as a challenge and brought discounted pots and forgotten buds of herbs from stall markets. Loaded ourselves with 'no peat' compost from the garden shop, we dug into the edges of the grass to make some space for flowers, trying to enrich the neglected broken soil of London.

Digging through the previous lives – the rusted nails, glass with softened edges from years underground, bits of rotten wood from old garden planters. We dig further down, gloved fingers passing worms.

In naive chaos, we plant, dig, sow seeds and hope. Squirrels take to the seeded planters, to take soil baths – twisting the compost, rolling on their backs, diving into the dirt. Upending the possibilities of carrots and lettuce, seeds scatter. I seek to touch each new plant. I brush the lavender leaves and coat my hands on a summer holiday; I smell the thyme on the breeze and think of dinner. The earth is baked from the sun and dryness smells clean, to me. I spray the garden in water with the hose creating neat arches in the sun and the cleanliness brightens and is fresh as the water hits the grass. Soil, newly damp, is enticing.

But now the rain is relentless. It soaks the ground. The air is rich with decay. The forgotten leaves, blown off trees that had drifted, now are stuck in corners of the garden with a whiff of must and death. The herbs and flowers I had planted in earlier weeks of sunshine seem to rejoice in this wetness, and continue to grow. Some in abundance. Red shiso surprises me, as does a blueberry bush. They seem to seek the elements, rain and wind is no match for their leaves stretching out, and out, and out.

Beneath a hot summer day, there is always rot. Rot, waiting for the rain, waiting to let life take shape. Where rot lives, growth finds a way to wiggle out.

I want to think of planting and growing new possibilities, new lives, new seasons. Where rot lives, we must find ways for lives to thrive.

I continue my daily intimacy with my plants, between rain spells. What will I grow in my garden next season?

Dowry Money Won't Bring the Groom Home

Zar Mose
Translated by Khairani Barokka
with translation from Baso Minang by JR Hadi

All of the blood flowing through your name is 'Pariaman groom'
Therefore, one day, you will be bought by the bride
with rupiah and gold
Just as tradition places a price
on the body that's contracted
On the body of a man whose footsteps will one day
forget the creaking of boards in the village at the surau and rumah gadang
Remember, boy, bajapuik is the cost of separation
that is offered by the bride
to a son and his mother
Alah bauriah bak sipasin, kok bakiek alah bajajak,
habih tahun baganti musim sandi adat jangan dianjak
Foreign, so foreign is Jakarta's soil that you forgot the gold
that paid for your body is the pouring sweat of a sea cucumber fisherman
who conveys his prayers in the middle of the night
under the moon, on a rickety boat
for Allah to place fresh seed soon
in the body of his daughter
How will you tell them
How will you let your in-laws know
that there will be no seed in the ocean of your wife's body
that will be sown and become fish that will travel the Java Sea
How could you have once said Iqra and now what you see
is only a glimpse of your feet behind the surau, playing jumprope
with the other little girls?
The scent of bungo rampai floods through the door of your mind
Knocking one by one on the gray rooms
that keep your old names
A year goes by and the season changes…
you have grown old, Sutan,
in others' lands, you hide, you don't remember that your mother awaits
come home if you still remember
that there is your mother who will bless you

kerokan

Khairani Barokka

let me see the skin of your back striped red
let me place cajuput oil between a coin and your masuk angin

the way wind is understood to enter our bodies,
shake down immunity, coat selves in shivers and germs

there is graceful gliding in the way we wear only sarung
and undies, lie face-down on the floor in surrender

to currency beating down effects of bodily vulnerability
into the shapes of tiger stripes, until our backs are plantain leaves

and we all know outsiders humoured to no end by masuk angin,
behaving as though only other ailments are real

as though money is, as though the coin used to rub wind's cloud
of illness from backs represents a truer god than these kind motions

the hands ignoring any lack of belief from those not seated
or prone, not ready to be opened on the ever-holding ground

About the contributors

Norman Erikson Pasaribu is a Bali-based writer, translator, and editor. Their poetry collection *My Dream Job* will be out in the UK in 2024 with Tilted Axis Press.

Tatevik Sargsyan is founding publisher and editor of Anamot Press, Trustee of the Poetry Translation Centre and a design strategist working with charities.

ko ko thett is a Burma-born poet and translator. He has published and edited several collections of poetry and translations in both Burmese and English. His poems are widely translated and anthologised. His translation work has been recognised with an English PEN award. ko ko thett's most recent poetry collection is *Bamboophobia* (Zephyr Press, 2022). He lives in Norwich.

kyi may kaung is a Burmese-American writer, scholar and activist. She contributed to the translation with ko ko thett.

Prahara Amelia is a queer writer and student. Her work explores themes of isolation, language, separation, and the asymmetries of girlhood. Born in Jakarta and raised in multiple cities, She is currently double-majoring in Comparative Literature and Asian Studies in South Korea.

Madina Malahayati Chumaera lives in Greater Jakarta. Her interests lie in the intersection between the humanities, the sciences, and everything in between. Her book *Contact Light: the void inside and out*–a collection of prose and poetry revolving around the concept of the human brain, outer space, and the connection between them–was published by Gramedia Pustaka Utama in October 2017.

Nurdiyansah is a queer writer and the author of *Rumah di Tanah Rempah* (Tales from the Spice Islands), a travelogue that explores cultural beauty and the history of colonialism through the tradition of spices in the Indonesian archipelago. He is based in Jakarta, works for Project Multatuli and spends his time collecting archives related to stories of queer individuals in Indonesia with Queer Indonesia Archive.

Mak Lin generously contributed her experiences of gender, sex work and community in Indonesia. She was in conversation with Nurdiyansah.

Caesar Abrisam is a writer. He lives in Jakarta.

Pychita Julinanda is a neurodivergent, genderfluid, transmasc, working class person active in media and cultural work. His interest revolves around liberatory politics in the collective practices of care and the radical imagination of the future.

Kristal Firdaus is a poet from East Kalimantan. Born in Tanjung Redeb, he has contributed to the Kalimantan poetry anthology *Cermin Lain di Balik Pintu Lamin*. His interest in contemplating body experience fuelled his passion for writing.

Ziggy Zezsyazeoviennazabrizkie is an Indonesian writer. She has authored numerous works including novels, short stories, and children stories. Her works have received awards and nominations, and her short stories have been translated to Japanese and English.

Pear Nuallak was dug out of Addington Hills in the late 20th century. Their first book, *Pearls From Their Mouth* (Hajar Press), was published in 2022.

Anna Sulan Masing is a writer, poet & academic based in London. She is one half of event series and podcast Voices At The Table, in 2021 she launched Cheese Magazine where she is Editor-in-Chief, and she is co-founder of communications agency A+F Creative.

Zar Mose is a digital imaging artist and the author of poetry collection *Galeri Hormonal*. Born and raised in Batusangkar, he is currently studying English Literature at University of Diponegoro, Semarang. His works explore queerness in poz, Minangkabau and Islamic landscape.

Khairani Barokka is a writer, poet and artist in London. She's a practice-based researcher, whose work centres disability justice as anti-colonial praxis. Among her honours, she was Modern Poetry in Translation's Inaugural Poet-in-Residence, the first non-British Associate Artist at the UK's National Centre for Writing, and an NYU Tisch Departmental Fellow, and is currently UK Associate Artist at Delfina Foundation and Research Fellow at University of the Arts London.

JR Hadi contributed a translation from Baso Minang, an Austronesian language belonging to the Malayic linguistic subgroup, which in turn belongs to the Malayo-Polynesian branch.

First published in the UK in 2024 by Anamot Press, London, UK.

ISBN 978-1-7393467-2-0

Printed and bound by TJ Books in Padstow, Cornwall, UK
Designed by Sukutangan

Supported by